BOOK TWO

You Are the Judge!

Michel Lipman, JD

Academic Therapy Publications
Novato, California 94947

Academic Therapy Publications
20 Commercial Boulevard
Novato, California 94947

International Standard Book Number: 0-87879-281-3

0 9 8 7

0 9 8 7 6 5

Contents

Introduction

Did you ever visit a law library? If you did, you would see what seem to be miles of bookshelves filled with books. You'd think there must be a million laws. And you'd be right. Our nation does make many laws. Also, each of our 50 states makes laws. Each county and city makes laws that are called "ordinances." And we have hundreds—more likely thousands—of bureaus making regulations.

How can anyone—even lawyers and judges—know them all? How can you possibly obey them all? Well, luckily, most of them aren't likely to concern you. For example, one set of laws says what kind of machines and equipment a manufacturer may sell to other countries. Another might regulate hours and wages in coal mines. Unless you get into these kinds of businesses, you won't ever need to know about them.

But there are laws that do affect you. You and others must obey them. Some give you important rights. Others give you important duties. Oddly, most of these laws come from two short pieces of writing—the Ten Commandments and the Bill of Rights of our country. Thousands of law books are filled with cases deciding people's rights and duties, all based on them.

In this short book, you will read about real cases in court, the kind you see on TV or read about in your newspapers. Names, places, and events are changed somewhat to assure privacy to the people involved. And we've used ordinary language where the real lawyers used legal language. To keep it short, we've cut and changed some of the actual procedures. But what you read is close to the way it really happened.

You will get a taste of the kinds of cases our courts rule on and discover how judges look at the facts. And you will learn to think like a judge! You'll see that what looks simple really isn't, that neither side is all right or all wrong. You will have to *balance* the rights and duties of the people.

Are you surprised that we don't give you right and wrong answers with these case problems? Don't be. You make your own right answers! You study the facts, listen to the arguments of attorneys for both sides, and hear the witnesses. Then you fill in to your own satisfaction the questions on the judge's "Think Sheet."

You think. You weigh the evidence. You try to balance one against the other. *And whatever you decide is right.*

Because—YOU WILL BE THE JUDGE!

CF and ML   1981

YOU ARE THE JUDGE
The Bleach and the Blonde

TODAY, YOU HAVE BEEN ASSIGNED a case brought by a customer against a beauty shop. Debra Drake was a dark-haired young lady who seems to have felt that blondes really do have more fun. So she went to the New Wave Shop to change the color of her hair.

Debra's attorney asks her, "Miss Drake, will you tell the court when and where you first discussed bleaching your hair with New Wave?"

"Yes, it was July 10th. I went to the shop and discussed the idea with Mrs. Trent, the owner. She told me they would use a chemical called 'Golden Halo.' But first, she said, they would give me a patch test to make sure I wasn't allergic to it."

"What did the test show?"

"That I was not allergic to 'Golden Halo.' So I told her to go ahead and bleach my hair as we'd planned, and she did."

"And you became a blonde?"

"Yes."

"What else happened as a result of the bleach?"

"Within a few hours my scalp began to burn. It became irritated and very painful. It took weeks of expensive medical treatment to return me to normal."

"During the course of your medical treatment, did you learn why this happened after your patch test showed no reaction?"

"Yes. It turned out that Mrs. Trent hadn't used 'Golden Halo,' for which I was tested. By mistake, she used a different bleach called 'Platinum Blonde.' It contained different chemicals than the first bleach. It was those different chemicals I reacted to."

Mrs. Trent's attorney now cross-examines Miss Drake. "Tell me, Miss Drake, were you ever allergic to anything before you went to the New Wave Shop?"

"Yes, when I was a small child, it turned out I was allergic to licorice jellybeans."

"So it's possible that something besides bleach caused this latest allergic reaction, is that right?"

"It's possible, but I doubt it."

"Isn't it possible that a shampoo or hair-set lotion might have caused a low-grade reaction that you didn't notice?"

"I suppose that's possible. I wasn't aware of it."

"Thank you, Miss Drake. That's all."

Now the attorneys sum up their cases.

Debra Drake's attorney says, "In this case, your honor, we have had testimony of medical witnesses. Their tests show that Debra is definitely allergic to chemicals in 'Platinum Blonde,' which was used by mistake for 'Golden Halo.' Also, the reaction took place within a few hours after 'Platinum Blonde' was used on her hair and scalp. She didn't use anything else during those hours, so the strong possibility is that the untested bleach caused the reaction. This was a negligent or careless act by the operator. Everyone who does a negligent act is responsible if someone is hurt as a result. So Miss Drake should get damages."

Mrs. Trent's attorney said, "It is true that someone doing a negligent act is responsible if someone is hurt as a result. Here we agree there was a negligent act—a mixup of bottles. And we agree Miss Drake was hurt. But we do *not* agree that one was the result of the other. We say it is not at all clear, nor is it proved that the untested bleach caused the irritation to her scalp. Miss Drake admits being allergic to at least one other substance, and it is possible she has other allergies as well. Mrs. Trent should not be ordered to pay damages."

You say, "Thank you for your statements, counsellors. I'll take the case under submission and let you know the court's ruling in a few days."

Now you are alone in your judge's chambers. You must find the answers to several questions so that you can decide the case, and be sure your decision is within the law. You must consider all the facts, and then complete your official Opinion and Order.

Judge's "Think Sheet"

What are the facts?

1. What did the owner do to test Debra Drake's hair and scalp?

_____

_____

_____

_____

2. What is an "allergy?" What is an "allergic reaction?"

_____

_____

_____

_____

3. Did Debra Drake say she had an allergic reaction to the chemical used on her head?

_____

_____

_____

_____

4. What happened to Debra Drake's scalp within a few hours after Mrs. Trent put the chemical on it?

_____

_____

_____

_____

5. How sure were the chances that the chemical caused the problem: 100%? 90%? 75%? 25%? No chance at all?

_____

_____

_____

_____

6. Was the chemical put on Debra Drake's hair the same kind of chemical that was used in the test?

_____

_____

_____

_____

7. If it wasn't the same, why was it used?

_____

_____

_____

_____

8. If there was a mix-up of the chemical bottles, who was at fault?

_____

_____

_____

_____

IN THE SUPERIOR COURT OF THE STATE, IN AND FOR THE COUNTY OF

MONROE

DEBRA DRAKE   )
)
     Plaintiff)
)
 vs   )   No. 507-83
)
HELGA AMSTEAD TRENT, doing)
business as, NEW WAVE SHOP)
)
     Defendant)

COURT'S OPINION AND ORDER

FOR JUDGMENT

   This suit was brought by a customer against the owner of
a beauty shop. The customer, Debra Drake, went to get her hair
bleached to a lighter color. The owner, Helga Trent, made a
patch test. This was to make sure the customer was not allergic
to the type of bleaching chemical to be used. The test showed
she was not allergic to "Golden Halo."

   However, the owner made a mistake. Instead of "Golden
Halo," she used "Platinum Blonde." This had different chemicals
in it. Miss Drake was not tested for "Platinum Blonde."

   After the bleaching was finished, she said her scalp began
to burn. This was within a few _____. She needed
                  hours / days
medical treatment in order to recover.

   Miss Drake said she _____ been allergic to any-
             had / had not
thing in the past.

   The question is whether her reaction was _____
                 very likely / not likely
due to the chemicals in "Platinum Blonde."

ORDER OF COURT

This court finds that the New Wave Shop _____
was / was not

negligent in mixing the bottles of bleach. It finds that the

chances of this mix-up causing the allergy reaction were _____
great / small

Therefore the court rules that the New Wave Shop

_____ pay damages to Miss Drake for her injuries.
must / need not

_____
JUDGE OF THE SUPERIOR COURT

YOU ARE THE JUDGE
The Dentist and the Disability Checks

YOUR NEXT CASE, Judge, presents this question of law: *when is work not work?*

Dr. Tusker is a dentist now in his sixties. When he was still a young man, he took out a disability insurance policy. This meant that if he were disabled and couldn't work at his profession for any reason, the company would pay him every month.

As he grew older, Dr. Tusker's hands became crippled through arthritis. He couldn't practice dentistry any more. So he sold his practice and stopped working. The insurance company began paying him each month as the policy said it would. In a few months, Dr. Tusker became very bored. He bought a half interest in a small dental laboratory which made dentures and plates for the patients of different dentists.

Then the insurance company stopped paying the dentist his checks every month. Dr. Tusker sued.

The attorney for the insurance company puts its agent on the stand.

"What was the reason you stopped paying Dr. Tusker his disability insurance?" the attorney asked.

"Because he was working," the agent said. "He went to the office at different times. He signed checks. He answered the phone, and he talked to dental suppliers. We understand that his knowledge of dentists and dentistry were quite valuable to the laboratory. Business doubled in a short while. Also, the value of his investment doubled."

"You say, then, that Dr. Tusker is working, though he is not working at his profession of dentistry?"

"That's correct. We consider that he is employed. He has made the company more valuable, and of course the part he owns in it is more valuable."

Dr. Tusker's attorney cross-examines the agent. "Mr. Damron, I understand you have investigated this case quite carefully. Tell me, did Dr. Tusker receive a salary for what he did?"

"No, sir, he did not."

"Did he keep regular hours, like 9 to 5, or come in every day?"

"No, I believe he came in when he wanted to and had no regular hours."

"But he wasn't practicing dentistry, was he?"

11

"No."

"Or using his hands to work on dentures or anything like that?"

"No. He can hold a pen or a telephone but cannot use delicate tools."

When the attorneys finish, you ask them to sum up their cases.

Dr. Tusker's attorney says, " 'Working,' in the way the policy reads, means doing something on a regular schedule and getting regular pay for it. My client was not getting paid; he was not on a regular schedule. He didn't have to come into the office at all if he didn't want to. It was entirely up to him. He was not an employee. He was an investor, or owner, looking after his investment. He still can't work at regular employment. He should continue to get his monthly checks from the insurance company."

The insurance attorney says, "Dr. Tusker is trying to eat his cake and have it, too. If he can work for a profit, as he is now doing, we shouldn't have to pay him for not being able to work. If he doesn't work because he can't, we will pay him. But he can't have it both ways. We claim he is actually working for compensation at the laboratory and isn't entitled to our checks."

"Thank you, gentlemen," you say. "Case will be taken under submission. Court is adjourned."

Now you are alone in your judge's chambers. You must find the answers to several questions so that you can decide the case, and be sure your decision is within the law. You must consider all the facts, and then complete your official Opinion and Order.

Judge's "Think Sheet"

What are the facts?

1. Why did Dr. Tusker stop working as a dentist?

_____

_____

_____

_____

_____

2. Did he get a salary for what he did at the dental laboratory?

_____

_____

_____

_____

3. If he got no salary, how did he benefit from what he did?

_____

_____

_____

_____

4. Why did the insurance company stop sending Dr. Tusker his monthly checks?

_____

_____

_____

_____

5. Is there a difference between earning money and owning something that grows in value?

_____

_____

_____

6. Can someone be "employed" if he isn't required to ever come to the office or do anything for the firm?

_____

_____

_____

_____

7. Was Dr. Tusker required to come to the laboratory that he partly owned?

_____

_____

_____

_____

8. What do you think "compensation" is?"

_____

_____

_____

_____

IN THE SUPERIOR COURT OF THE STATE, IN AND FOR THE COUNTY OF

MONROE

ARCHIBALD TUSKER, D.D.S.   )
)
          Plaintiff   )
)
    vs   )   No.   518-83
)
ALPHA OMEGA INSURANCE   )
COMPANY   )
)
          Defendant   )

OPINION OF THE COURT AND ORDER

FOR JUDGMENT

    This case was brought by Dr. Tusker, a policy-holder,
against the Alpha Omega Insurance Company. Arthritis in his
hands forced Dr. Tusker to give up the practice of dentistry.
He then invested some money in a dental laboratory. He was
not required to do anything, but to make his investment more
valuable, he did help out. His knowledge of dentistry and of
other dentists helped the laboratory get more business and make
more money.

    Alpha Omega had been paying the dentist disability in-
surance each month, because he could not work at his profession.
After he became interested in the laboratory, the insurance
people stopped the payments. They said he was employed and
therefore had no right to any more checks.

    A person who is legally disabled _____ still
                                       may / may not
be able to get around and do some useful things. It seems clear
that Dr. Tusker _____ hold a regular job, or prac-
                      could / could not
tice as a dentist. If he could, the decision in this case
_____ be the same.
would / would not

15

Another point: the laboratory made a profit, which bene-
fited Dr. Tusker. But it could just as well have had a loss.
Then he would get _____ benefit. When one is working
                    some / no
on most jobs, he or she _____ paid whether the
                        gets / does not get
company makes money or loses it.

ORDER OF COURT

The court finds that Dr. Tusker _____ working
                                was / was not
for wages by using some of his skills and talents for the laboratory he partly owned. Therefore the court orders that Alpha
Omega Insurance Company _____ Dr. Tusker his
                         pay / not pay
monthly disability checks.

_____
JUDGE OF THE SUPERIOR COURT

YOU ARE THE JUDGE
The Shoe Stock and the Storm

YOUR CASE TODAY, JUDGE, involves a stock of shoes. Nora Black had worked for a large department store. After a few years, she decided to open her own store, specializing in women's shoes. It wasn't easy to find the right location. Finally she found one that she liked. She signed a lease and put in her stock. Business was good—but Nora soon found there were other problems. She finally filed suit against her landlord, Dennis Lenhart.

In court, Nora's attorney asks her, "When was the first time you heard about the water leakage problem, Miss Black?"

Nora says, "At the time we talked about the lease—before I moved in. Mr. Lenhart said there'd been trouble about water in the basement, so I had a wooden platform built, about seven inches up from the floor. I used the space to store new shoe stock."

"Did the platform protect your stock?"

"Not entirely. There was some seepage from the winter rains. As a result, the shoes became moldy. I told Mr.Lenhart, and he said he would try some water-proof paint to keep out the water. That didn't work. Then he had some drainage ditches dug and installed two pumps. That helped some."

"Did you have any trouble after that?"

"Yes. Then we had a really bad storm. The worst in years. My basement flooded to a height of six feet. And of course my entire stock of shoes was ruined."

Mr. Lenhart's attorney cross-examines Nora.

"Miss Black, you say Mr. Lenhart warned you about the danger of seepage. He tried water-proof paint, dug ditches, installed pumps to keep the water out. Now, were these things done in a careless or unworkmanlike manner?"

"I wouldn't say that. What he did was well done. It's just that nothing he tried worked."

When the evidence is all in, you ask the attorneys to sum up.

Miss Black's attorney says, "Under the terms of the lease, Miss Black's landlord wasn't legally bound to do anything about the basement. But once having started to waterproof it, he was obliged to finish it. Miss Black relied on his efforts to protect her stock of shoes. His efforts failed—and she should be able to get her costs back from him."

17

Mr. Lenhart's attorney says, "Miss Black knew there was a water problem when she first talked to Mr. Lenhart about the lease. He told her there was. But she moved in anyway. Mr. Lenhart can't be held responsible for her shoes just because he tried to help her. He volunteered his work; he didn't have to do it. And what he did, he did well. He shouldn't be called on to pay."

"Thank you, counsellors," you say. "Case submitted. Court is now adjourned."

★ ★ ★

Now you are alone in your judge's chambers. You must find the answers to several questions so that you can decide the case and be sure your decision is within the law. You must consider all the facts and then complete your official Opinion and Order.

Judge's "Think Sheet"

What are the facts?

1. Did Nora know there was a water problem at the time she signed the lease for her shoe store? Did it seem serious?

_____

_____

_____

_____

2. What did she do about it?

_____

_____

_____

_____

3. Did she have a problem with her stock after that? What was it?

_____

_____

_____

_____

4. What did the owner of the property, Mr. Lenhart, do to help keep water out?

_____

_____

_____

_____

_____

5. Did he do these things in a careful, workmanlike manner?

_____

_____

_____

6. Did any of the things he did improve the situation?

_____

_____

_____

_____

7. What happened when an unusually heavy rainstorm came along?

_____

_____

_____

8. Did the lease say that Lenhart had to waterproof the basement?

_____

_____

_____

_____

1 IN THE SUPERIOR COURT OF THE STATE, IN AND FOR THE COUNTY OF

2   MONROE

3 NORA BLACK,   )
)
4   Plaintiff)
)
5   vs   )   No.   522-83
)
6 DENNIS B. LENHART,   )
)
7   Defendant)

8

9   OPINION OF THE COURT AND ORDER

10   FOR JUDGMENT

11   In this matter, Nora Black sued Dennis B. Lenhart, her

12 landlord, for damages to her shoe stock. The damage came after

13 Lenhart had taken a number of voluntary steps to stop leakage.

14 It appears Miss Black was warned about seepage before she leased

15 the property. She attempted to meet this problem by building a

16 platform for her stock. This was not entirely satisfactory as

17 the shoes became moldy.

18   When an unusually bad storm struck, the basement flooded

19 to a height of six feet. The stock was ruined. Miss Black sued.

20   Under the lease, Mr. Lenhard _____ required to fix
                                        was / was not

21 the leaks. However, he did try. He tried waterproof paint,

22 ditches, pumps. These _____ work.
                            did / did not

23   Should Mr. Lenhard have done more to waterproof the base-

24 ment? He had no way to test his work in advance. He did his work

25 well. He _____ be sure that what he did would keep
              could / could not

26 out water.

27   Also, Miss Black was warned there _____ possible
                                            was / was no

28 problem. She _____ there was an element of risk in
                  knew / did not know

                                21

leasing that particular store.

ORDER OF COURT

The court finds that Lenhard _____ legally required
was / was not
to waterproof the basement. He _____ negligent.
was / was not
He _____ mislead Miss Black. Therefore he_____
did / did not   must / need not
pay for the damages to her shoes.

_____
JUDGE OF THE SUPERIOR COURT

YOU ARE THE JUDGE
The Bandit and the Black Belt Belter

YOUR HONOR, the first case today involves the safety of a customer in a grocery store. Charles Ray is suing the Scott Street Supermarket. He says he was injured when a bandit held up the market and fired a shot at him.

Charles' attorney says, "Will you tell the court, Mr. Ray, what you did at the time you entered the market on the day in question?"

"Yes. My wife was in bed with a virus infection, and I went in to pick up a few things for her. Milk, boullion cubes, orange juice, stuff like that. I had these in the basket and was heading for the check-out counter when I saw this holdup attempt."

"Will you describe what you saw?"

"There was this short, heavy-set guy at the check-out stand. He was holding a gun—a revolver. Pointing it at Bill Fleming, the clerk. I know Bill slightly. Black belt in karate. Young, strong, tough. I saw him grab the guy's gun-arm, then chop at his neck. But the guy caught it on his shoulder. He pulled loose and fired at Bill. Bill ducked behind the counter, and the shot mised. I knew there was a phone at the back of the store and started for it to call the police. The guy must have seen me. I heard another shot, felt a sting in my leg, and fell to the floor."

"Do you know if the bandit was ever caught?"

"Not as far as I know."

Now the store's attorney cross-examines Charles. "When the scuffle started at the check-out counter, would you say the bandit looked surprised or startled or angry?"

"That's hard to say. Surprised, I guess. Or scared."

"Didn't you realize that by starting for the phone, you called the bandit's attention to yourself?"

"I was mad. Mad and scared. I wanted to see this bum caught."

"If you had remained quietly where you were, wouldn't you say the bandit would not have seen you? Then you wouldn't have been injured?"

"I suppose so."

Charles' attorney sums up his case. "The owners of a place of business have a legal duty. It is to have a reasonably safe place for their customers. They must take precautions to see that people who come in are protected. Charles here was a customer. The clerk courageously but foolishly fought with the bandit. The angry, frightened man ran, shooting wildly and hitting Charles. Had the clerk simply handed over the cash box, chances are this shooting would not have occurred."

The Scott Street Supermarket's attorney said, "The market does have the duty of keeping a reasonably safe place. But it has no duty to protect against every possible kind of danger. Some things just cannot be foreseen. That was the case here. Also, Charles added to his own danger by starting for the phone. He himself attracted the bandit's attention, so he should not be entitled to damages."

At this point, Judge, you thank the attorneys and take the case under submission. You will study the file and the evidence, and make your decision.

Now you are alone in your judge's chambers. You must find the answers to several questions so that you can decide the case, and be sure your decision is within the law. You must consider all the facts, and then complete your official Opinion and Order.

Judge's "Think Sheet"

What are the facts?

1. What steps have you noticed markets and stores taking to protect customers both inside and on their parking lots?

_____

_____

_____

_____

2. What instructions should the owner of a store give the clerks in the event of a holdup?

_____

_____

_____

_____

3. Do you think the clerk here, Bill Fleming, received any instructions about holdups?

_____

_____

_____

_____

4. Are store holdups so rare that it is not reasonable to expect they will happen?

_____

_____

_____

_____

5. Is it likely that Bill Fleming's unexpected resistance angered and frightened the bandit?

_____

_____

_____

_____

6. Is it likely that Charles Ray, the customer, would not have been shot if he hadn't started for the telephone?

_____

_____

_____

_____

IN THE SUPERIOR COURT OF THE STATE, IN AND FOR THE COUNTY OF

MONROE

CHARLES GARNER RAY   )
)
              Plaintiff   )
)
     vs   )   No. 523-83
)
SCOTT STREET SUPERMARKET   )
)
              Defendant   )

OPINION OF THE COURT AND ORDER

FOR JUDGMENT

    In this matter, Mr. Ray sued the Scott Street Supermarket
for injuries. He was shot by a bandit during a holdup attempt.

    Mr. Ray was a distance from the checkout stand, walking
toward it with the items he had selected. He saw the bandit
point his gun at the clerk. He saw the clerk grab the bandit and
try to take the gun away. He heard one shot and saw the clerk
duck behind the counter. Then he started for the telephone to
call police. The bandit saw him, fired, and hit him in the leg.
Mr. Ray now sues the market, for injuries.

    It is settled law that people who have businesses must take
reasonable steps to protect their customers. Most stores keep
their parking lots well graded and free of obstacles. They in-
struct clerks to mop up spills and remove bits of fruit or vege-
tables on the floors that might be slippery and make people fall.
Larger stores often hire security guards. They guard both the
cash and the people who come in to shop. Smaller stores cannot
usually afford guards.

1   In Mr. Ray's case, there was no guard. We may say the

2   clerk, Bill Fleming, did not act wisely regarding his own safety.

3   But Fleming could not anticipate that by tackling the bandit his

4   customer would be shot.

5   So we conclude that Fleming's action _____ the
                                          was / was not

6   reason that Ray got shot.

7   There is also the problem of Ray's action in starting for

8   the telephone. This was also a courageous act. It _____
                                                        did / did not

9   expose him to danger.

10   One more point. Fleming's attack on the bandit was clearly

11   to protect his employer's cash. The protection of property like

12   cash is _____ important than the protection of people.
             more / less

13   ORDER OF COURT

14   It is the finding of this court that the Scott Street

15   Supermarket _____ take reasonable precautions to see
                 did / did not

16   that customer Ray was protected. Therefore Ray _____
                                                     should / should not

17   win damages from the store.

18

19

20   _____
                                JUDGE OF THE SUPERIOR COURT

21

22

23

24

25

26

27

28

The Firebug and the Fire

YOU HAVE BEEN HEARING evidence in the case of Ann Blanken against Pacific and Orient Insurance Company. Ann's husband lost his life in a fire in the paint store he operated.

The husband, Hugh Blanken, had taken out a life insurance policy for $25,000 in favor of Ann shortly after they were married six years before. The Pacific and Orient refuses to pay because the paint store fire was started by Hugh himself.

Ann is testifying now.

Her attorney asks, "Mrs. Blanken, you knew at the time you married Hugh Blanken that he did not have a very good reputation, did you not?"

"So everyone told me. Especially my mother. He had run with the wrong kids and been in trouble several times."

"Did he change after you married him?"

"In my eyes, he did. But he did have trouble holding jobs. He was very likeable and got them easily enough. But he seldom lasted more than a few months in a job."

"Why did he decide to go into business for himself?"

"Well, he happened to pick a horse that came in at 80 to 1 and had several thousand dollars. He invested that in the paint store."

"Was it successful?"

"No. It lost money almost from the first day."

"Did you have any idea he might set the shop on fire to collect the fire insurance money?"

"I did—but I hoped I had discouraged the idea. He said to me one day it was lucky he had $100,000 insurance on the place because there had been so many fires around town lately."

"What did you say to that?"

"I said I knew what he had in mind, and he'd better forget it. I said if he did what he was thinking, I would walk out and never come back."

The other attorney asks only one question in cross examination. "Mrs. Blanken, how did your husband meet his death?"

"One night when I was at the movies, he appears to have gone to the store and into the basement with a can of gasoline and some matches. It seems he didn't know the power of a gasoline explosion."

Ann's attorney says, "Your honor, Mrs. Blanken made no claim for the insurance on the paint and wallpaper store. However, she does claim payment under a separate life and accident policy taken out years earlier. The $25,000 is payable when the insured meets death through violent and accidental means. Mr. Blanken's death from explosion and fire was certainly violent and accidental."

The insurance company's attorney says, "It's true that Mr. Blanken's death was accidental in a sense. But it was an accident that he brought about himself through his own dangerous and illegal act. Arson is one of the worst criminal acts. The benefits he was after should not be allowed to go to anyone he named in the policy."

Now you are alone in your judge's chambers. You must find the answers to several questions so that you can decide the case, and be sure your decision is within the law. You must consider all the facts, and then complete your official Opinion and Order.

Judge's "Think Sheet"

What are the facts?

1. Did Hugh Blanken expect to get insurance money if his paint and wallpaper store caught fire and burned?

_____

_____

_____

_____

2. How did the store happen to burn?

_____

_____

_____

_____

3. Did Ann Blanken have any part in Hugh's crime of arson?

_____

_____

_____

_____

4. Was there a second insurance policy on Hugh's life?

_____

_____

_____

_____

5. Was it payable to Ann?

_____

_____

_____

_____

6. Why didn't the insurance company want to pay Ann for the insurance on Hugh's life?

_____

_____

_____

_____

7. When did Hugh take out the life insurance policy?

_____

_____

_____

_____

8. At the time he took out the life insurance policy, do you think he intended to buy a paint store and burn it down?

_____

_____

_____

_____

IN THE SUPERIOR COURT OF THE STATE, IN AND FOR THE COUNTY OF

MONROE

ANN BLANKEN   )
)
              Plaintiff   )
)
      vs   )   No.   535-83
)
PACIFIC AND ORIENT INSURANCE)
COMPANY   )
)
              Defendant   )

OPINION OF THE COURT AND ORDER

FOR JUDGMENT

Ann Blanken, widow of Hugh Blanken, has sued Pacific and Orient. Her husband had a $25,000 insurance policy on his life. She was to get the money if he met death through violence and accident.

Hugh had a paint store that was losing money. He decided to burn it down for the insurance. One night he went into the basement with a can of gasoline. He attempted to set the fire. There was an explosion, and he died in the fire.

The life insurance company refused to pay the $25,000. They say Ann shouldn't get the money because this wasn't really an accident; it was an event caused by Hugh's criminal act of arson.

It is true that the law usually won't let someone benefit from the criminal act of someone else. To do so would encourage crime.

However, what a person intends is an important part of a crime. Here Hugh got the life insurance policy shortly after the couple were married six years before. The evidence shows that he

worked at a number of jobs, and did not buy the paint store until recently. He _____ intend to commit arson at the time
did / did not

he took out that life insurance policy.

ORDER OF COURT

The court finds that Hugh Blanken _____ meet
did / did not

his death by accidental and violent means. It finds that at the time he applied for the life insurance policy he _____
did / did not

intend to set fire to a store. Pacific and Orient Insurance Co. is ordered to _____ $25,000 with interest to Ann
pay / not pay

Blanken.

_____

JUDGE OF THE SUPERIOR COURT

The Fisherman and the Fish

YOUR PRESENT ASSIGNMENT, JUDGE, is the State against George Wise-As-Fox. The charge against Mr. Wise-As-Fox is fishing out of season with an illegal net.

The government's evidence shows that Anton Adams, a fish and game warden, was patrolling the river. He discovered a large nylon net, 130 feet long. The salmon were running up river, and thousands of them were caught in the net.

Nearby stood George Wise-As-Fox, raking in the floundering fish and putting them in baskets. Officer Adams immediately arrested Mr. Wise-As-Fox. Now the matter is in your court.

Mr. Wise-As-Fox's attorney is questioning him.

"Will you tell us your racial origin and the tribe, if any, to which you belong?"

"I am an American Indian. My tribe is the Lemhi. My people have lived in this place for hundreds of years."

"Will you tell us about the treaty the Lemhi have had with the United States Government since 1857?"

"Yes. The treaty gives our tribe the right to hunt and fish in this area for all time without limit."

The government's attorney now cross examines.

"Mr. Wise-As-Fox, at the time this treaty was signed, how did members of your tribe catch the salmon that swam in this river?"

"They used bows and arrows, sometimes baited fishhooks and lines, sometimes hand-held nets. Sometimes the fish ran so thick they caught them with their hands."

"Yes. But you use a net, do you not? How many fish have you caught with this net since the run of salmon started?"

"I don't know how many fish. Close to two and a half tons."

"Thank you, Mr. Wise-As-Fox. That is all."

Now the attorneys sum up. The government's attorney says, "Your honor, there is no doubt the Lemhi Indians have a treaty and that Mr. Wise-As-Fox is a Lemhi Indian. However, the laws of this state limit fishermen to two salmon per day. This limit was put on to preserve the salmon so they'll continue to spawn. The object is to have a supply of salmon for years ahead. If we allow a few people—such as the Indians—to fish on such a great scale with huge nylon nets, there soon won't be any salmon for anyone, white or red. The government has no objection to the Indians' fishing out of season with traditional equipment. But not with this kind of net. We think this man is outside the treaty and should be convicted."

Wise-As-Fox's attorney says, "The government's concern over conservation is something rather new. This treaty over the rights of Indians is quite old. What was a good bargain once may become a bad bargain as the years go by. That's too bad for those concerned—but the courts ordinarily do not have the power to remake their agreement. My client should not be convicted."

You say you will consider the case and adjourn court.

Now you are alone in your judge's chambers. You must find the answers to several questions so that you can decide the case, and be sure your decision is within the law. You must consider all the facts, and then complete your official Opinion and Order.

Judge's "Think Sheet"

What are the facts?

1. Was George Wise-As-Fox fishing in the traditional manner of his people?

_____

_____

_____

_____

2. Does it seem to you that if all members of the Lemhi tribe fished with huge nylon nets, it would seriously affect the salmon run?

_____

_____

_____

_____

_____

3. Should a treaty of the United States have greater weight in court than a state law?

_____

_____

_____

_____

4. Who were the people that made this treaty?

_____

_____

_____

_____

5. Should one party to a treaty be able to change it without the consent of the other side? _____

_____

_____

_____

6. Plainly neither the government or the tribe thought about nylon nets when they made that treaty in 1857. If the salmon are to be conserved, how do you suggest the government go about getting the Indians not to overfish the river?

_____

_____

_____

_____

IN THE SUPERIOR COURT OF THE STATE, IN AND FOR THE COUNTY OF

MONROE

THE UNITED STATES OF AMERICA)
)
Plaintiff)
)   Crim. No. 247-84
vs)
)
GEORGE WISE-AS-FOX)
)
Defendant)

OPINION OF THE COURT AND ORDER

FOR JUDGMENT

The evidence in this matter shows that George Wise-As-Fox,
a member of the Lemhi Indian tribe, was fishing for salmon with
a huge nylon net, out of season. The state law limits a fisher-
man's daily catch to two salmon, and sets the days on which he
may fish.

Wise-As-Fox, however, claims that these limits do not apply
to him. He cites an 1857 treaty between his tribe and the government of the United States. The treaty gave the tribe fishing
rights forever.

Treaties have a higher standing in law than even formal con-
tracts. There_____ anything in the treaty that said
              was / was not
how the Indians should fish. High court cases hold that Indian
treaties are as effective and binding as those with foreign
nations. Where they conflict with state law, the state law must
give way.

Had there been no treaty, Wise-As-Fox _____
                                        would / would not
be in violation of the law. But since there is a treaty giving

1 him and his fellow tribesmen greater rights than other citizens

2 of the state, he _____ _____ in violation.
                        is / is not

3   ORDER OF COURT

4   In view of what has been said, the court finds the defendant

5 _____ and he shall be _____.
        guilty / not guilty   discharged / sentenced

6

7

8

9   _____
                                         JUDGE OF THE SUPERIOR COURT

10

11

12

13

14

15

16

17

18

19

20

21

22

23

24

25

26

27

28

The Painter and the Public

TODAY, JUDGE, YOUR case has to do with character assassination. The artist, Peter Paul Rembrandt, has sued the Mayor of South Dorcas. Rembrandt says the Mayor slandered him—or ruined his good name.

So far, the evidence shows that on June 11 the City of South Dorcas held an art show. Among the exhibitors was Peter Paul Rembrandt. Peter had a growing reputation for his wild, futuristic paintings. And he sold many of them at good prices to collectors and others who thought they would go up in value.

The Mayor's attorney questions him.

"Mayor Rockwell, you attended the gala opening night with other city officials, contributors, reporters, and others. As you walked through the gallery with this group, you came upon Mr. Rembrandt's painting. What was your reaction to it?"

"Well, it was a shock! I'd never seen anything so wild in my life! Frankly, I was appalled that our committee had allowed it to be shown."

"What did you do, Mayor Rockwell?"

"I ordered it taken out at once. And it was. After a few minutes delay, what with the television cameras and all, we moved along to see the other paintings."

Mr. Rembrandt's attorney now cross-examines the Mayor. "Mayor Rockwell, you say you came to my client's painting, 'Life Inside a Mousetrap,' and that it was a shock to you. Now, you made some remarks to the people around you, didn't you?"

"I suppose I did."

"Will you repeat those remarks, please?"

"Well, I think I said it was indecent. And a monstrosity. And maybe a few other things I don't quite remember."

"And you said all this in a very loud voice, didn't you, knowing there were reporters present with tape recorders and television cameras?"

"I probably spoke loudly enough to be heard. I may have shouted a bit. I was, as I said, quite shocked."

"Is it true that on the following day your remarks and your picture appeared in newspapers and on television screens all over the country?"

"Yes, there was considerable coverage."

Now the attorneys sum up.

Peter Paul Rembrandt's attorney says, "Your honor, in this case, we recognize the right of people to comment on works of art and other artistic creations. The Mayor was entitled to say 'Life Inside a Mousetrap' was a bad painting. But he is *not* entitled to say the artist is a bad person when in fact he is not. Here the Mayor said 'it was indecent.' We claim that is a reflection on the painter. We showed in earlier evidence that Mr. Rembrandt is a family man, a respected citizen in his town, a church-goer, a person who has never been involved with police or with scandal of any kind. The publicity given the Mayor's remarks has damaged his good reputation. People no longer buy his paintings as much as they did before."

The attorney for the Mayor says, "It is the Mayor's duty to protect the peace and act for the well-being of the people. Here he seemed to feel they should be spared the shock he felt. So he acted as a public official and ordered it removed. Public officials, acting in their public capacity, are immune from lawsuits for what they do."

Now you take the case under submission and adjourn court.

Now you are alone in your judge's chambers. You must find the answers to several questions so that you can decide the case, and be sure your decision is within the law. You must consider all the facts, and then complete your official Opinion and Order.

Judge's "Think Sheet"

What are the facts?

1. If a work of art is indecent, does that mean the artist who created it is also indecent?

_____

_____

_____

_____

2. Why do you suppose that on this opening night there were reporters and news people there with the Mayor?

_____

_____

_____

_____

3. Do you think the fact that there were reporters around had anything to do with the Mayor's remarks?

_____

_____

_____

_____

4. Was the Mayor acting as a censor in ordering 'Life Inside a Mousetrap' removed from the art gallery?

_____

_____

_____

_____

5. Do you believe that the duties of a mayor usually include the duty to censor paintings?

_____

_____

_____

_____

6. Would there be a reflection on the artist's character if the mayor had only said the painting was ugly?

_____

_____

_____

_____

IN THE SUPERIOR COURT OF THE STATE, IN AND FOR THE COUNTY OF

MONROE

PETER PAUL REMBRANDT   )
)
                   Plaintiff)
)
         vs   )   No. 531-83
)
EMERY G. ROCKWELL, MAYOR   )
OF SOUTH DORCAS, AND THE   )
CITY OF SOUTH DORCAS   )
)
                   Defendant)

OPINION OF THE COURT AND ORDER

FOR JUDGMENT

The artist, Peter Paul Rembrandt, filed suit against Emery

Rockwell for slander, or character assassination.

The Mayor referred to the artist's painting as "indecent"

in the presence of reporters and others. He underscored his

feelings by ordering the painting removed. The artist says his

reputation both as a painter and as a person has been damaged.

The law protects the good reputation of people. If someone

says, untruthfully, that another person is a communist, or is

racially prejudiced, or has a social disease, or is a thief, or

is a hypocrite, he can be successfully sued.

However, the law also protects the right to comment, even

critically, on films, paintings, plays, TV shows, operas, singers,

and so on.

Here the Mayor had a right to criticize Rembrandt's paint-

ing. He _____ have a right to critize the artist, as
          did / did not

when he referred to the work as "indecent."

There is another point here. In ordering "Mousetrap"

45

removed, the Mayor was acting as a censor. Mayors do not ordinarily have censorship as one of their official duties. So here
he _____ acting as a city official who cannot usually
         was / was not
be sued.

ORDER OF COURT

 Peter Paul Rembrandt _____ slandered by Mayor
                                  was / was not
Rockwell. The Mayor _____ be sued. Therefore
                         may / may not
Rembrandt _____ entitled to damages for what the
               is / is not
Mayor said and did.

_____
JUDGE OF THE SUPERIOR COURT

The Schemer and the Skis

YOUR PRESENT CASE, YOUR HONOR, is a suit by Jennifer Hobbs against High Sierras Sporting Goods Company. She claims the company owes her money for an idea.

The company is national distributor for a less expensive ski that is manufactured in Europe and imported. It was designed for young, beginning skiers. It had been selling well in some other countries. Here, the company advertised the product as "Designed for the Beginning Skier." And they sold poorly.

Jennifer Hobbs was experienced in advertising. She met with Homer Webley, president of High Sierras Sporting Goods Company. Now she is suing.

Jennifer's attorney asks her, "Please tell the court, Miss Hobbs, what you and Mr. Webley talked about at that meeting."

"I told him I knew his skis weren't selling well. I told him the problem was in his advertising. I said I could tell him how to correct the problem. We agreed that if I told him my plan, and he accepted it, his company would pay me the reasonable value of it."

"What was that plan, Miss Hobbs?"

"It was to change the advertising and not use the old slogan. That was 'Designed for the Beginning Skier.' I told Mr. Hobbs people didn't want to be seen on the slopes with skis that tagged them as *beginners*. Skiing is a status sport. How you look is as important as how good you are."

"How did you suggest he change his advertising?"

"I said the line he should use was 'Looks, Feels, and Runs Just Like the Professionals.'"

"Did Mr. Webley accept your idea?"

"No. He said he didn't think he liked the concept. So I left."

"Did that end the matter?"

"No. I learned that Mr. Webley mentioned my plan to his sales manager. The manager liked it. He tried it out in three cities. And sales picked right up. When I found out about this, I went to see Mr. Webley again. He said they were evaluating the results. He said they didn't know at that time if the plan had any value or not. So he wouldn't pay me."

On cross-examination, the ski company's attorney asked, "Mr. Webley didn't say he wouldn't ever pay you, did he?"

"No. He said he might pay me later if the idea worked out."

Following the evidence, the attorneys argued the case.

Jennifer's attorney said, "Ideas are property. They can be bought, sold, or stolen. The courts have held that when an idea is submitted with the understanding it is to be paid for if used, that understanding will be enforced. And the price is the reasonable value of the idea."

The company's attorney said, "In a case like this, there's no way to tell if an idea is acceptable. Not unless you test it. Well, the company is testing it. Once they get all the information together, it can make a decision. Miss Hobbs has filed this suit too soon. The suit should be dismissed."

You thank the attorneys and adjourn court.

★　　★　　★

Now you are alone in your judge's chambers. You must find the answers to several questions so that you can decide the case, and be sure your decision is within the law. You must consider all the facts, and then complete your official Opinion and Order.

Judge's "Think Sheet"

What are the facts?

1. Does it seem, on the basis of the evidence here, that Jennifer had a valuable idea?

_____

_____

_____

_____

_____

2. Was it a plan that could have been sold to any other company?

_____

_____

_____

_____

3. Did Mr. Webley agree to pay Jennifer if he used the plan?

_____

_____

_____

_____

4. A "test" means that a company puts its product in local stores and advertises it. Then they can see how well it might do in other cities. Is testing an idea a "use" of it?

_____

_____

_____

_____

5. Should Webley have tested the idea without getting Jennifer's permission first?

_____

_____

_____

_____

6. Can an idea be called property, just as houses, autos, money, books, and other objects are called property?

_____

_____

_____

_____

IN THE SUPERIOR COURT OF THE STATE, IN AND FOR THE COUNTY OF

MONROE

JENNIFER HOBBS,   )
)
                  Plaintiff   )
)
        vs   )   No.   527-83
)
HIGH SIERRAS SPORTING   )
GOODS COMPANY   )
)
                  Defendant   )

OPINION OF THE COURT AND ORDER

FOR JUDGMENT

Here Jennifer Hobbs has filed suit against the sporting
goods company for using her idea without paying her.

She had thought of an original plan to boost the company's
sales of skis. She told the firm's president the plan on his
promise to pay her if he used it. The firm does not deny that
he made the promise. Or that the firm tested the idea in three
cities and that it was successful.

The defense is that though successful, they do not know
yet if the plan has any value. Their position is they cannot
pay her the reasonable value until they know what that is.

There is no doubt that the firm has to pay Jennifer. Ideas
are property. Original ideas have value. Some ideas, like this
one, cannot be copyrighted or patented. But the law will protect the person with the idea just the same. The person must
take the right steps. That is, tell the possible user that he
has an idea, and he will tell what it is. He must let the possible user know that payment is expected, if the idea is used.

51

Then if there is use, the money is due. Very often it is

_____ to say ahead of time how much this should be.
easy / hard

What is a "reasonable" amount depends on how much value the

plan has for the one using it.

The claim of the company that it cannot set this value

until further study _____ all bad. If it pays before
is / is not

it knows how much good it will do, the amount may be too small.

Or too large.

Regardless of that, the company _____ acted
has / has not

properly. Testing may be proper. But testing _____ part
is / is not

of use. It seems clear that if the company wanted to test, it

_____ have gotten Jennifer's permission in advance.
should / should not

She could have chosen to let them test without payment. Or

she could have insisted on partial or full payment at that time.

They _____ give her this opportunity. In this they
did / did not

were _____ .
right / wrong

ORDER OF COURT

It is the order of this court that the sporting goods

company _____ Jennifer Hobbs for her idea. Because
pay / not pay

the reasonable value cannot be decided at this time, the court

will keep this case open. Part payment will be made now. The

balance will be paid later, when the value of the idea is clear.

_____
JUDGE OF THE SUPERIOR COURT

YOU ARE THE JUDGE

The Survey and the Seller

YOUR NEXT CASE, JUDGE, is unusual—but such things happen every once in a while. Osmund Peterson is suing Alma Gregg for improvements he put on her property.

Osmund's attorney says to him, "Mr. Peterson, please tell the court how you came to buy the house in question."

Osmund says, "I was looking for an old place to fix up and sell. Mr. White had just the kind of house I was looking for. He was elderly, a little absent-minded, and had been a builder years before. He said he'd bought several lots on the same block, maybe thirty years back. He built on three of them. He said he'd sell me the one I was interested in. It was a two-story, seven-room house. We made a deal. Then I went to work on it, remodeling and modernizing and painting. I put in a lot of time and money. Twenty-five thousand dollars in materials alone."

"What happened to the house when you finally finished your work?"

"Well, then a Mrs. Finley showed up. She said the house I bought wasn't Mr. White's at all. She said she sold him a lot, all right, but it wasn't this one."

"In other words, she claimed Mr. White built the house on the wrong lot?"

"Exactly. I didn't believe it at first. But I got a lawyer to check, and he said her claim was right. There were several empty lots on that block. Mr. White never had it surveyed. He just assumed this one was his and went ahead and built on it."

"Now, Mr. Peterson, you're willing to give up the house, but you want to be paid for your work and materials. Is that right?"

"Yes. Mr. White did return the money I paid for it, but I'm still out of pocket for what I did."

Now Mrs. Finley's attorney cross-examines Osmund Peterson. "Mr. Peterson, did you, at the time of buying this property, hire a surveyor to check the property lines?"

"No, sir, I did not. I assumed that a house which the seller had occupied for years was really his."

"Did Mrs. Finley at any time authorize you to do this work on her house?"

"No. I didn't know it *was* her house until after the work was done."

This concludes the testimony. Now you tell the attorneys they may sum up.

Osmund's attorney says, "Your honor, Osmund acted in good faith. The mistake was not his, but White's, who'd built the house years before. It's not fair that he should go to all this work and expense and for the owner then to get all the benefit without a nickel cost. Further, this house had been on her lot for more than thirty years—and she never once came near the lot to see its condition. Under these circumstances, Osmund should be paid."

Mrs. Finley's attorney says, "No law says an owner has to inspect his property at any time. Actually, Osmund Peterson was a trespasser. He had no right to be on the property at all. There would have been no problem at all if he'd taken the trouble and small expense to have a survey made by a professional surveyor. He is not entitled to any payment for what he did."

"Counsellors," you say, "this is a difficult case. I'll take it under submission and give an opinion in the next few days."

Now you are alone in your judge's chambers. You must find the answers to several questions so that you can decide the case, and be sure your decision is within the law. You must consider all the facts, and then complete your official Opinion and Order.

Judge's "Think Sheet"

What are the facts?

1. Why is this an unusual case?

_____

_____

_____

_____

2. Why do you think Mr. White, the original builder of the house, put it on Mrs. Finley's lot?

_____

_____

_____

_____

3. Why didn't Osmund Peterson have a survey made to make sure he had the right lot?

_____

_____

_____

_____

4. Should Mrs. Finley have checked on her lot during the years she owned it?

_____

_____

_____

_____

5. If Mrs. Finley wins this case, will she own a remodeled house without having to pay anything at all for the improvements?

_____

_____

_____

_____

6. Did she know the house was being built or remodeled?

_____

_____

_____

_____

7. Were Osmund and the first owner, Mr. White, trespassers?

_____

_____

_____

_____

8. Would the error have been discovered if either Osmund or White had gotten a surveyor to check the property lines?

_____

_____

_____

_____

IN THE SUPERIOR COURT OF THE STATE, IN AND FOR THE COUNTY OF

MONROE

OSMUND PETERSON   )
)
               Plaintiff   )
)
       vs   )   No. 512-83
)
ARABELLA B. FINLEY   )
)
               Defendant   )

COURT'S OPINION AND ORDER

FOR JUDGMENT

The testimony here shows that Osmund Peterson did a great deal of work and improvement on a house which belonged to Arabella B. Finley. He did not know it was hers at the time. He had paid for it and thought it was his. The fault was the original builder's who seems to have been confused about which lots on the block were actually his. It is clear that Mrs. Finley did not tell Peterson he could improve the house, or even know what he was doing.

Now, because of White's and Peterson's mistakes, Mrs. Finley has a valuable house on her land for which she has paid nothing. The question here is whether she should be made richer at the expense of Mr. Peterson.

Peterson_____ he had no right to build on
              knew / did not know
the lot in question. He_____a trespasser. He
                         was / was not
_____ have a survey made to find out where his
      did / did not
property lines really were. If he had done so when he bought
from White, he_____have known what his rights were.
                would / would not
Not all states have the same law. But in this state, the

57

law is that people who mistakenly improve other peoples' property without knowing the right boundary or property lines, are not entitled to be paid for what they do. Here Osmund Peterson improved Mrs. Finley's property _____ the right
knowing / not knowing
property lines.

ORDER OF COURT

The order of this court is that Mr. Peterson _____
should / should not
get his money from Mrs. Finley.

_____
JUDGE OF THE SUPERIOR COURT

The Homemakers and the House

THE CASE BEFORE YOU, JUDGE, has been brought by a young married couple. Carol and George both worked. They saved their money and bought an old house. There was a lot wrong with it, but the price was right. They both did a lot of the work needed. And it began to shape up. All but the floors, which were badly rotted.

The couple's attorney asked George, "You decided you'd need an experienced contractor for that job, you've said. Now who did you hire?"

"Well, we got Bruce Watkins, who said he was experienced. The price he gave was fairly reasonable, and we told him to go ahead."

"Who was to furnish the materials for the job?"

"He was. Lumber, cement, nails, everything. And any workmen needed to finish the work."

"How well did he do the work, Mr. Davis?"

"Not well. He made a number of mistakes that even I, as an amateur builder, could have avoided. He had to do some parts over. He was pretty unhappy about that. So was I."

"Then what happened?"

"Then the whole floor collapsed, and some of the wall fell with it."

"Did you discuss this with Mr. Watkins?"

"I certainly did! I told him he'd have to rebuild the floor and wall. He said he would—if I paid him an extra $9,000. He said he was losing money on our job, and he wasn't going to take that kind of a loss. I refused to pay any more than I'd agreed, and he walked off. I had to hire someone else—and it cost us a bundle."

Bruce Watkins' attorney cross-examines George Davis. "Did you ever, at any time, ask Mr. Watkins if he was a licensed contractor?"

"No."

"Why not?"

"It didn't occur to me. I was only interested in getting a good job done for a reasonable price."

"You knew, of course, that this state has a law requiring anyone who takes a general building contract to be licensed, didn't you?"

"Well, I suppose I did. I think I more or less assumed Mr. Watkins was licensed."

"But you never took the trouble to ask him. Is that right?"

"That's right."

Now, Judge, all the witnesses have told their stories. You tell the attorneys they may argue the case.

The attorney for George and Carol says, "Your honor, this is a simple case of a broken agreement. Bruce Watkins said he would do a job. He agreed it would meet the plans and specifications he was given. And that meant in a workmanlike manner. His work fell apart, and he refused to make it good. He should pay the Davises what it cost them to hire someone else."

Watkins' attorney says, "Your honor, it isn't as simple as all that. Bruce Watkins is not a licensed contractor. Starting the job for the Davises was an illegal act. And the Davises were parties to that illegal act. They knew the law; that was admitted here. They could have asked Watkins about his license. And if they weren't satisfied with his answer, they could have telephoned the State Contractors' Licensing Board for public information. By failing to even ask, they took part in evading the law. Therefore, they cannot get money damages from my client."

You say, "Thank you, gentlemen. Court is adjourned. You should have the court's decision shortly."

Now you are alone in your judge's chambers. You must find the answers to several questions so that you can decide the case, and be sure your decision is within the law. You must consider all the facts, and then complete your official Opinion and Order.

Judge's "Think Sheet"

What are the facts?

1. Was Bruce Watkins a good, experienced builder?

_____

_____

_____

_____

2. Was he licensed to build for other people for pay?

_____

_____

_____

_____

3. Whose fault was it that Carol and George's floor caved in?

_____

_____

_____

_____

4. Did Bruce Watkins complete the job in a satisfactory manner?

_____

_____

_____

_____

_____

5. Was it necessary for George and Carol to find out if Watkins was a licensed contractor and builder?

_____

_____

_____

_____

6. Were they at fault for not finding out?

_____

_____

_____

_____

7. Is this fault enough to keep them from getting damages for the caved-in floor?

_____

_____

_____

_____

8. Did the completed floor rebuilding cost Carol and George more than they had agreed to pay?

_____

_____

_____

_____

IN THE SUPERIOR COURT OF THE STATE, IN AND FOR THE COUNTY OF

MONROE

GEORGE DAVIS and CAROL DAVIS,   )
his wife,   )
)
                    Plaintiffs   )
)
        vs   )   No.   497-82
)
BRUCE WATKINS, doing business   )
as WATKINS HOME REPAIRS   )
)
                    Defendant   )

COURT'S OPINION AND ORDER

FOR JUDGMENT

This case came on for trial on April 19th. The Davises
are home owners. Bruce Watkins agreed to repair their floors,
and the Davises agreed to pay him a fixed price for the work.
Watkins was not highly skilled in his work, made a number of
mistakes, and finally allowed the floor to collapse. He refused to repair the damage he created, unless he received more
pay. Watkins is not a licensed contractor, and is in violation
of state law.

Watkins, through his attorney, claims that the Davises
are also in violation. He says they could easily have found out
he wasn't licensed. For that reason, he says, the court should
leave the parties where they find them. In effect, he says,
where both sides violate the law, there can be no damages.

It is true that when both sides are law-breakers, the court
will not aid either of them. Are the Davises lawbreakers?

The contractor licensing law in this state was designed to
protect the public. Contractors must pass a stiff test. The
test weeds out those who don't know enough to be good builders.

It _____ protect the public in that builders may build
     does / does not
only when they know what they are doing. The Davises _____
                                                          had / had no
reason to think Watkins was not licensed. They _____
                                                     did / did not
have a duty to find out if a person advertising himself as a

builder is actually state-licensed.

If the Davises actually knew that Watkins was not licensed,

but hired him anyway, the case _____ be different.
                                   would / would not
Then they _____ get damages.
             could / could not

ORDER OF COURT

The order of this court should be that George and Carol

Davis _____ damages from Bruce Watkins.
         win / do not win

_____

JUDGE OF THE SUPERIOR COURT

The Hoodlums and the Heart

THIS CASE, YOUR HONOR, is one of murder. The accused are two young men, Timothy Harlan and Frank Darwin. The victim was Samuel Tupperman, a retired man.

The testimony has shown that Timothy and Frank were young men with long records of minor offenses. They are 19 and 20 years old. On January 12, they strong-armed a pair of high school boys and took two toy pistols from them.

On January 13, two young men with stockings over their faces met Samuel Tupperman as he was coming out of his apartment house. They pointed guns at him and ordered him back against the wall.

One of the young men—later identified as Timothy—snarled at the victim. He said, "Hand over your wallet and be quick about it and maybe you won't get hurt."

The district attorney questions Armand Fort, who saw the incident from a window just across the street. "Mr. Fort, what did you see happen at that point?"

"Well, sir, Mr. Tupperman was leaning back against the building like he could hardly stand. I saw him hand his wallet to one of the punks. Then they ran."

"What did Mr. Tupperman do?"

"He just stood there for a minute like he didn't know what to do. Then he just sort of slumped down to the sidewalk. I called the police, then ran over to try and help him. He was unconscious or maybe dead then. I don't know. Anyway, the police came, and an ambulance, and took Mr. Tupperman away. I heard later he died of a heart attack."

"You said earlier you saw the guns these defendants used. Could you tell if they were real or toy?"

"I thought they were real. They looked just like regulation army forty-five caliber automatics."

The attorney for the accused cross-examines. "Mr. Fort, at any time during this hold-up, did either Tim or Frank touch Mr. Tupperman?"

"No, sir."

"They didn't shove or push him around in anyway?"

"I didn't see anything like that."

At this point, the attorneys sum up.

The district attorney says: "This victim had heart trouble. He died as a direct result of fright. The fright was plainly caused by this hold-up. There was a sudden, abrupt confrontation. Then the pointing of two realistic looking pistols. And the threat of violence. The defendants are guilty of murder in the first degree—an unintentional killing during the commission of a felony."

The opposing attorney says: "If the court please, no physical force was used on the victim. The defendants didn't even touch the victim. They couldn't have shot him because their guns were only toys. They couldn't reasonably foresee that their victim might have a bad heart. Any ordinary victim would not have died. They only intended to frighten him into handing over his wallet without protest. They should be acquitted of the murder charge."

You say, "Thank you, counsellors, for your presentations. The case is submitted. I'll rule on it shortly."

Now you are alone in your judge's chambers. You must find the answers to several questions so that you can decide the case, and be sure your decision is within the law. You must consider all the facts, and then complete your official Opinion and Order.

Judge's "Think Sheet"

What are the facts?

1. Did Samuel Tupperman die as a result of the fright he got during the holdup?

_____

_____

_____

_____

2. Did Timothy and Frank know Tupperman had a heart condition?

_____

_____

_____

3. Would it have made any difference if they had?

_____

_____

_____

4. Did they intend to kill him?

_____

_____

_____

_____

5. Does it make any difference that the guns were toys and not the real thing?

_____

_____

_____

_____

6. Is it a defense of their acts to say they did not use physical force?

_____

_____

_____

_____

7. Is pointing a gun at someone who believes it real a threat of physical force?

_____

_____

_____

_____

8. Do you think this crime comes under "special circumstances" which might carry the death penalty?

_____

_____

_____

_____

9. What do you think their punishment is likely to be if they are convicted?

_____

_____

_____

_____

IN THE SUPERIOR COURT OF THE STATE, IN AND FOR THE COUNTY OF

MONROE

THE PEOPLE OF THE STATE   )
)
             Plaintiff   )   Crim. No. 147-83
)
        vs   )
)
TIMOTHY HARLAN and FRANK DARWIN)
)
            Defendants   )

OPINION OF THE COURT AND ORDER

FOR JUDGMENT

The evidence shows that the the two defendants held up Samuel Tupperman, an elderly person with a bad heart. They used toy pistols which appeared real. They did not shove or push the victim around. They took his wallet and ran. They were seen running by a police officer who arrested them.

The defendants make the point that they didn't intend to harm Mr. Tupperman. They just wanted his money.

The fact is, they were committing a felony. The law says that anyone who commits a felony intends all the possible and probable results of that felony. Here it was quite possible that some ill or feeble person would die as a result of fright. And that is exactly what happened here. Whatever harm came about from the defendants' acts -- including murder - - was their responsibility.

ORDER FOR JUDGMENT

The defendants _____ the death of Samuel
                        caused / did not cause

Tupperman. They_____ have actual intent to kill
                did / did not

him. Whether they did or not, the law says they did and here

the law _____ be applied. Both defendants are there-
        must / must not
fore _____ of murder in the first degree.
        guilty / not guilty

_____
JUDGE OF THE SUPERIOR COURT

The Mailman and the Muzzle

THE PRESENT CASE, YOUR HONOR, is a suit by James Joyce Hemingway, a mail carrier, against the Civil Service Commission.

The Commission suspended Mr. Hemingway for 90 days because of a letter he wrote.

Several people were running for state senator. Mr. Hemingway knew one of the people running and felt he should make his feelings known to other voters.

He wrote a letter to a major newspaper in the area. In it he said, "Mr. Daly is a fine person. But he is completely inexperienced in finance, politics, or business. I'm sure his intentions are excellent—but intentions are not enough in so important a job as senator. I hope he will withdraw from the primaries."

Mr. Daly, who saw the letter published in the newspaper, not only didn't withdraw, he filed charges against Hemingway with the Civil Service Commission. The Commission oversees the hiring and firing of people who work for the Post Office and other government offices.

Mr. Hemingway's attorney asks him, "Do you often write political letters?"

"No. This is the first time that I can recall."

"Did you write as part of any organized political action?"

"No, it was just something I did on my own."

"No one asked you to write it? No one paid you to write it?"

"Certainly not."

The government's attorney cross-examines. "Mr. Hemingway, how long have you worked as a mail carrier for the government?"

"Ten years."

"During that time, did you hear anything about the Hatch Act, which prohibits federal workers from taking part in politics?"

"Yes, but I didn't think that applied to writing letters."

Now the counsel for the parties sum up.

The government's attorney says, "If the court please, writing letters to a newspaper for possible publication is a violation of the law. The law was passed because workers in government offices were sometimes forced into supporting one candidate or another. It's really for their own protection because it allows them to vote their own choice."

Hemingway's attorney says, "Your honor, the right to vote is fundamental. But just voting isn't enough. A citizen has the right to express his opinions. Part of the election process is for people to talk and exchange information and ideas. Hemingway is entitled to that right, which does not conflict with the law."

You take the case under submission, and will prepare your decision.

Now you are alone in your judge's chambers. You must find the answers to several questions so that you can decide the case, and be sure your decision is within the law. You must consider all the facts, and then complete your official Opinion and Order.

Judge's "Think Sheet"

What are the facts?

1. Should a citizen be entitled to write letters about his political opinions?

_____

_____

_____

_____

2. If Hemingway had not been a government worker, would there have been any question about his letter?

_____

_____

_____

_____

3. Do you think the rights of citizenship include telling what you think about candidates and proposals as well as just voting?

_____

_____

_____

_____

4. Why was the Civil Service Commission involved in this case?

_____

_____

_____

_____

5. What did the Civil Service Commission do to Hemingway?

_____

_____

_____

_____

6. Why do you suppose the attorneys wanted to know if Hemingway wrote this letter on his own or as part of a group effort?

_____

_____

_____

_____

IN THE SUPERIOR COURT OF THE STATE, IN AND FOR THE COUNTY OF

MONROE

JAMES JOYCE HEMINGWAY   )
)
         Plaintiff   )
)
vs.   )
)   No. 521-84
CIVIL SERVICE COMMISSION)
)
         Defendant   )

OPINION OF COURT AND ORDER

FOR JUDGMENT

James Joyce Hemingway is before the court. He wants an order to make the Civil Service Commission remove his suspension.

He was suspended by the Commission which said he violated the Hatch Act. This Act limits what government workers can do in elections. They cannot take part in organizations that work with political aims.

The federal constitution - and most state constitutions - guarantee freedom of speech to all of us. The liberties of speech, press, and assembly are fundamental rights. Laws that take away these rights are violations of due process.

But these freedoms don't mean we can always say anything we want. As one Supreme Court Justice said, "The right to free speech doesn't include the right to shout "Fire" in a crowded theater." Where there can be danger to the public, the rights can be limited. The question here is whether Mr. Hemingway's acts were such that they could be limited by the Hatch Act.

Here, testimony shows that Mr. Hemingway wrote a single, unsolicited, unpaid-for letter. This _____ the kind of

is / is not

political activity that the Act is against. It _____

would / would not

be different if his letter had been part of an organized

political effort. While the Act limits, it _____

does / does not

completely prohibit all political talk or action by government

workers like Hemingway.

ORDER OF COURT

The Civil Service Commission _____ ordered to

is / is not

reinstate Mr. Hemingway.

_____

JUDGE OF THE SUPERIOR COURT

Glossary

ADJOURN THE COURT: The same as closing business for the day. Or the court may say, "We'll adjourn for lunch. Come back at two o'clock."

ARGUE THE CASE: The attorneys tell the judge why they think their client should win. Sometimes the facts, or the law, or both, are very complicated. They try to explain it as they see it. The judge listens and then makes up his own mind. We also say that the attorneys—and sometimes the judge—will SUM UP THE CASE.

COMPENSATION: Being paid for some act against you. If you're injured on a job, you may get some money. This is *compensation*. Or if the state takes your house to put a freeway through, it pays you compensation, which is the value of your property.

COURT IS IN SESSION: The court is "open for business." Usually this means trying a case. But it can also mean a time for signing orders, sentencing, or hearing arguments of the attorneys.

DISABILITY: When a person is sick or hurt so he or she can't get around well, this is a disability. People who have good jobs or who practice law, medicine, dentistry, or nursing sometimes take out disability insurance. Then, if they get sick or hurt and can't work, the insurance company pays them so much every month.

DISTRICT ATTORNEY: The "D.A." as he or she is often called, represents the State. In some places he is called "State's Attorney." He handles criminal cases. He may also act for the State in some civil cases, such as condemnation of real estate for a new highway or state building.

EVIDENCE: Something that furnishes proof. This may be what a witness tells the court under oath. Or it may be an object, such as a pistol, a bent automobile fender, or a contract to buy a house. There are many complicated rules about what is or is not the kind of evidence the court will accept.

ILLEGAL, ILLEGALITY: This means doing something (or not doing something) that the law says is wrong. Parking your car next to a fireplug is an illegal act. Not getting a license to drive if you do drive is an illegal act.

INTENT: The state of mind in which you do something. In criminal law, the district attorney must show that you meant to do an act that the law says is a crime. Example: It's a criminal act to steal something from a department store. Suppose that without thinking, or because his arms are loaded with packages, a customer puts an item in his pocket and leaves without paying for it. If he *meant* to slip the item past the check-out clerk, the court could say that's the *intent,* and carrying the item is the *act;* the two together make up a crime. But if he didn't mean to leave without paying for the item, there is no crime.

JUDGMENT: A court's formal opinion. The opinion includes an order to do or not to do something. The person must do what he is told, such as pay the money, or his money or property can be taken away. Or in child support cases, he must pay the money if he is able to or go to jail. This is about the same as TO RULE FOR OR AGAINST.

JURY: A group of people who listen to the case and then decide what the facts are. They tell the judge what they think the facts are, and the judge then makes his ruling. For many years, juries always had 12 people. But recently there have been some eight-person and six-person juries, and they seem to work just as well. A person *must* be given a jury trial in criminal cases if he wants one. It's the same in some civil cases, too. But there need not be a jury if both sides agree there will not be. Most cases do not have juries. Then the judge acts as both judge and jury.

LEASE OR LEASING PROPERTY: The same as renting. A lease fixes the amount of rent and may limit the number of people and set other terms such as no pets or children, and so on.

ORDER OF COURT: About the same as ruling for or against someone. Sometimes an order of court stays in effect for a long time as when the court orders a father to pay monthly support money to his infant until the child is 18.

TAKING THE CASE UNDER SUBMISSION: When the judge says this to the attorneys, it means he will think about it for a while, study the law, and give his opinion later. Sometimes the attorneys may say, "We'll submit the case on the evidence," or "We'll submit on the pleadings." This means, "This is everything we want to give you, Judge. Now it's up to you."

TESTIMONY: This is what witnesses say in court under oath. That is, they swear to tell the truth, the whole truth, and nothing but the truth. Then the attorneys—and sometimes the judge—will question them. "I saw Mr. Peters sign that paper on August 1st in the evening." That is *testimony.* If it later turns out that the witness was deliberately lying, he can be sent to jail for perjury.

TO RULE FOR OR TO RULE AGAINST: A judge may order someone to jail or order someone to pay someone else or order that someone need not go to jail or pay. That's *ruling*, just as a baseball umpire decides who is or isn't out.

TREATY: This is a written agreement between nations. It may say they aren't going to fight any more. Or it may set fishing rights or say that one nation may use the ports of another or set borders.

TRESPASSER: One who goes on someone else's land or into his house without any right to do so. This is illegal, and the owner may sue him for any damage he might do. But a person may have a right to go if he is a business visitor, if he has been invited in some way, or permitted to enter.